PETAL TO THE METAL

Written by **PAUL TOBIN**
Art by **RON CHAN**
Colors by **MATT J. RAINWATER**
Letters by **STEVE DUTRO**
Cover by **RON CHAN**

DARK HORSE BOOKS

PETAL TO THE METAL

PLANTS vs. ZOMBIES

President and Publisher **MIKE RICHARDSON**
Editor **PHILIP R. SIMON**
Designer **BRENNAN THOME**
Digital Art Technician **CHRISTINA McKENZIE**

Special thanks to LEIGH BEACH, GARY CLAY, SHANA DOERR, ALEXANDRIA LAND, A.J. RATHBUN, KRISTEN STAR, JEREMY VANHOOZER, and everyone at PopCap Games.

Scholastic edition: July 2016
ISBN 978-1-50670-258-2

10 9 8 7 6 5 4 3 2 1
Printed in the United States of America

DarkHorse.com | PopCap.com

No plants were harmed in the making of this comic. Numerous zombies, including all the ones who can drive, pump gas, or unfold a map, however, definitely were.

NEIL HANKERSON Executive Vice President TOM WEDDLE Chief Financial Officer RANDY STRADLEY Vice President of Publishing MICHAEL MARTENS Vice President of Book Trade Sales MATT PARKINSON Vice President of Marketing DAVID SCROGGY Vice President of Product Development DALE LaFOUNTAIN Vice President of Information Technology CARA NIECE Vice President of Production and Scheduling NICK McWHORTER Vice President of Media Licensing KEN LIZZI General Counsel DAVE MARSHALL Editor in Chief DAVEY ESTRADA Editorial Director SCOTT ALLIE Executive Senior Editor CHRIS WARNER Senior Books Editor CARY GRAZZINI Director of Print and Development LIA RIBACCHI Art Director MARK BERNARDI Director of Digital Publishing

"TIRESSS."

"BRAINSSS."

"BRAINSSS."

"BIG, FAT TIRES!"

"OF LATE, WE'VE BEEN HAVING TROUBLE WITH STIKEWEEDS DESTROYING OUR TIRES, BUT MY BRILLIANT MIND HAS DEVISED A SOLUTION!"

"COME THIS WAY. I'LL SHOW YOU MY LATEST INNOVATIONS."

"OH, BUT---WATCH YOUR HEAD. I'M TRYING OUT A NEW TRAINING SYSTEM."

THOOP THOOP

THOOP

WHAP

"SO...YOU'RE A REPORTER FOR BRAIN 2, THE WEEKLY BLOG ABOUT ALL THINGS ZOMBIE?"

"BRAINZZZ."

"BRAAAINS?"

CHOMP CHOMP CHOMP

"OUR DAYS EARLIER..."

CLICK!

CLKK CLKK CLKK

CLKK CLKK CLKK

CLKK CLKK CLKK

BRRRRRNS.

"—TWELVE MINUTES AND SEVEN SECONDS!

SHUNK!

THOK

THE WORLD RECORD FOR A PIT STOP IS ELEVEN SECONDS, BUT MY TRAINED ZOMBIES CAN DO A FULL PIT STOP IN ONLY—

BUT HERE...HERE... IS THE START OF MY NEW ARMY!

AN ARMY OF RACECAR DRIVERS AND ZOMBIE MECHANICS!

ALTHOUGH I SUPPOSE THAT LAST BIT IS REDUNDANT.

AS SOON AS WE WORK OUT ALL THESE MINOR PROBLEMS, WE WILL RULE THE STREETS!

AND THOSE WHO RULE THE STREETS RULE THE CITY!

AND THOSE WHO RULE THE CITY... RULE THE CITY!

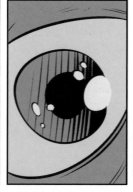

FULL GARGANTUAR POWER!...

YES! WE HAVE ACHIEVED...

THOOM THOOM THOOM

BRRAAINSS!

YOU CAN'T HAVE TOO MANY ENGINES!

AND THESE TWO.

AND THIS ONE.

AND THIS ONE.

LET'S ADD IN THIS ENGINE!

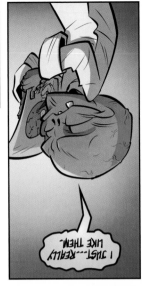
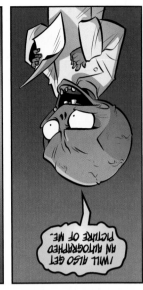

CAREFUL CROSSING THE STREET, PRINCESS WAILTIME.

YIP! YAP!

YIP! YAP!

Welcome to the bucolic streets of

Neighborville!

The city known for peace, friendly citizens, and quiet enjoyment.

BRNZZZ

RRROAR!

Welcome to the bucolic streets of

Neighbor

The city known for peace citizens, and

Also, the okasional Zombie Invazion!!

SCREEAA!

VZOOOM

AHHH!

AHHH! AGAIN!

PRINCESS WAILTIME?

YIP!

OH, NO! ZOMBIES! WHAT COULD POSSIBLY BE WORSE?

BRAINS!

BRAINS!

GOOD ENOUGH.

IS THIS THAT AMNESIA AVENUE SOAP OPERA? I HATE THIS SHOW. CHANGE THE CHANNEL!

AND....

YOU'RE ON.

CAR AGAINST CARJ LOSER HAS TO LEAVE THIS CITY FOREVER!

GROBBLE CRUNCHY PLOPPLE FUZZ-TOWER LOOOOFEN!

HE CHALLENGES YOU IN THE NAME OF ALL THAT IS GOOD, IN THE NAME OF ICE CREAM, AND SUNFLOWERS, AND DONKEY EARS!

AND HE CHALLENGES YOU FOR THE SCIENTIFICALLY SOUND REASON OF...DUH.

HE CHALLENGES YOU!

AND, UH.... ALSO....

...DO YOU HAVE ANY BUBBLEGUM?

UNCLE DAVE ASKS....

LORPPLE GLORN LOG SPLARN!

ERRPT!

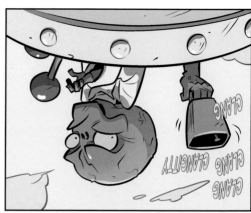

SHINE!

SHINE!

SHINE!

SHINE!

I'M SORRY, DO YOU MIND?

RIGHT, SO WE CAN SLEEP IN SHIFTS.

YOU GO FIRST.

HMMM.

GRAWS BAGGLE.

FLURNT! FLOOSWHISTLE!

UNCLE DAVE SAYS HE HASN'T SLEPT IN FIFTEEN YEARS, AND IT HASN'T AFFECTED HIM AT ALL.

I CAN'T BELIEVE I'M SAYING THIS, BUT...ZOMBOSS IS RIGHT.

WE'VE BEEN GOING FOR HOURS AND HOURS NOW, AND SOONER OR LATER, WE'LL NEED SLEEP.

A Sasquatch sighting!

Competitive squirrel naming!

GOING ON CAT-WATCHING EXPEDITIONS!

IS THAT A SPECKLED SNOOZER?

WELL, IT COULD BE, BUT IT LOOKS MORE LIKE A SPOTTED DAYTIME NAPPER TO ME.

SELLING HOMEMADE LEMONADE!

LEMONADE! ONLY A DOLLAR!

IT'S FOR A GOOD CAUSE!

It's LeMonAde! all proceeds go to the Handshake Academy

PLAYING BADMINTON!

OH, JOLLY GOOD SHOT!

INCOMING!

GOSSIPING ABOUT COOKIES!

SO JUST LAST WEEK SHE WAS EATING A CHOCOLATE CHIP COOKIE, BUT THEN LAST NIGHT SHE WAS EATING A PEANUT BUTTER COOKIE, AND THEN HER COUSIN, YOU KNOW, MARY SUE, DID YOU KNOW THAT I SAW HER AT THE MALL WITH SOME SUGAR COOKIES, AND THEN AFTERWARD I WAS AT THE PARK AND HER PICNIC TABLE HAD OATMEAL COOKIE CRUMBS BUT SHE SAID IT WAS JUST SHORTBREAD COOKIE CRUMBS, AND I WAS ALL LIKE, MARY SUE, I DO THINK I KNOW OATMEAL COOKIE CRUMBS WHEN I SEE THEM.

EIGHBORVILLE. THE CITY OF SMILING FRIENDS, WHERE PEOPLE GATHER TOGETHER FOR SUCH SIMPLE PASTIMES AS...

FRIENDSHIP BRACELET EMPORIUM

STOP

Rolly's Posh Pancakes

WORST OF ALL....

PLUS....

AND THERE'S A LOOMING CLUB THUMPER!

LOOK OUT! IT'S A FINE SPECIMEN OF A RED-TIED BRAIN GRABBER!

AND ALSO....

NOOOOON

NO! STAY AWAY FROM MY COOKIE COLLECTION!

AND SO....

OH, THIS IS WRETCHED!

INCOMING!

AND ALSO GETTING INVADED BY ZOMBIES.

FRIENDSHIP BRACELET EMPORIUM

AND...CRAZY DAVE IS GONE, WHICH ALL MEANS...

AND...THE PLANTS ARE OUT OF TOWN!

AND...NATHAN TIMELY ISN'T HOME!

BUT...PATRICE BLAZING ISN'T HOME!

WE NEED HELP!

WITH A FINAL RESULT OF...

"...WE STILL HAVE TO KEEP MOVING!"

"...OUR SUN-POWERED CAR DOES GREAT IN THE DESERT, BUT...."

LUCKILY, THEY'RE WAY BACK THERE, AND....

YEAH! I THINK SO!

WHAT'S HE SAYING?

HE WANTS TO KNOW IF WE'RE STAYING AHEAD OF THE ZOMBIES.

GRIPPLE FLOOP FLOUNDERGRAM?

ICE-CREAM RACE!!!

MEANWHILE...OODLES OF MILES AWAY....

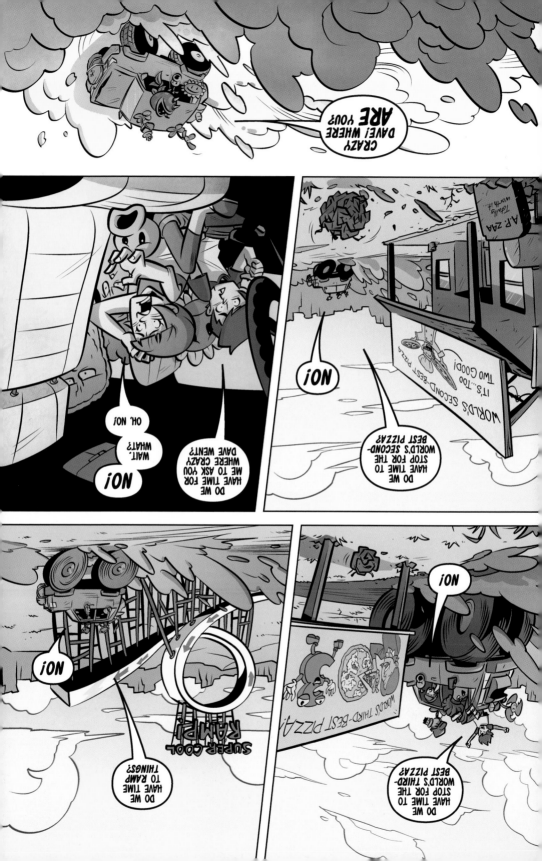

AND...SOON.

THWOOOSH!

THERE. NOW YOUR CARS ARE GONE. THE RACE IS EFFECTIVELY OVER.

THERE'S NO WAY YOU CAN MAKE IT BACK TO NEIGHBORVILLE IN TIME.

YOU'RE STRANDED!

BUT...JUST BECAUSE WE'RE NOT SUPER CRUEL...

...HERE'S A MAP ON HOW TO GET HOME.

BYE!

PEEL-OUT!

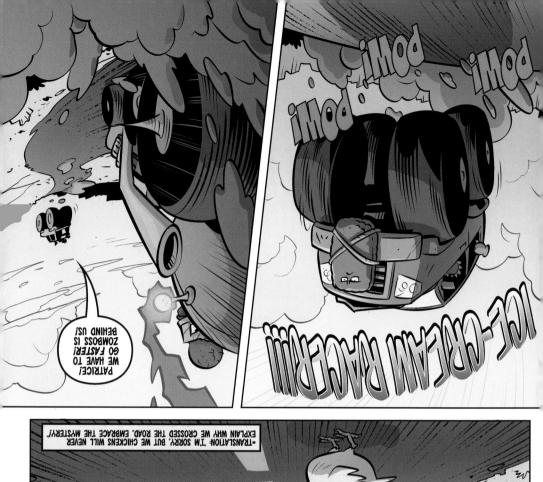

"...AS LONG AS THOSE OTHER ZOMBIES WE STRANDED...

"...DON'T FIND THEIR WAY BACK TO THE CITY IN TIME."

YEP. EVERYTHING WILL BE FINE NOW, BECAUSE WE HAVE MORE THAN ENOUGH FIREPOWER TO WIN THE BATTLE FOR NEIGHBORVILLE....

THAT SHOULD DO THE TRICK.

WHICH WAY?

MUNCH

MUNCH

MUNCH

FREE BRAINS!

FREE POPSMARTS

FREE BRAINS?
FREE POP SMARTS?
BUT... WHERE?

I THINK WE'RE OKAY.

REVERSE

THUMP

REVERSE

THUMP

THIS IS ALL WORKING OUT, FRED. IF WE CAN KEEP THE ZOMBIES RACING, THEY'LL RUN OUT OF FUEL AND BECOME STRANDED...

...EASY PICKINGS FOR US IN OUR SOUPED-UP SUN-POWERED CARS. I'M BETTING THEY'RE NOT SMART ENOUGH TO FIGURE IT OUT.

SCREEEECH!

PUT!

PUT!

PUT!

PUT!

BRAAAAINSS!

Go!

SPLURK

SPLAPP!

HUFF! HUFF! HUFF!

HFF!

HFF!

PLANTS VS. ZOMBIES
RELAY RACE!

FASTER! THEY'RE CATCHING UP!

NATE, YOU DON'T ACTUALLY HAVE TO YELL OUT THE SOUND EFFECTS.

ERRRT!! SCREEECH!! VROOOOMM!!

VRROOOM!

SCREEECH!

ERRRT!

CAUTIONARY NOTE:
NEVER SAY THINGS
LIKE THIS!

I THINK WE
CAN WIN THIS NOW!
WE HAVE THEM ON
THE RUN! NOTHING
CAN POSSIBLY GO
WRONG!

ATTACK!

WHOMP!

ATTACK!

THEY'RE
SITTING
DUCKS!

SMASSSHHH!!

WE CAN'T STOP THIS THING! EVEN THE TRIPLE TALL-NUT WALL IS USELESS! WHAT ARE WE GOING TO DO?

SCURRY!

SCURRY!

SCURRY!

RUN!

RUN! RUN!

RETREAT!

GULP.

RAWRR!

RAWRR!

T'HOOP!

T'HOOP!

TWEEN

P-TOO

P-TOO

FIRE! WE NEED TO TAKE THAT THING DOWN!

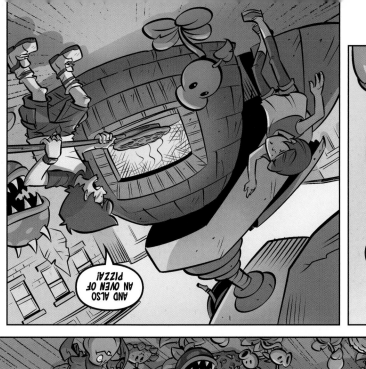

AND ALSO AN OVEN OF PIZZA!

HE'S TURNED THE DINO-PIG INTO A ROBOT! INTO AN ENGINE OF DESTRUCTION!

BRAINS?

UNCLE DAVE?

CRAZY DAVE?

HUH?

FUMBLE

NOOOO!

OOP! AAP!

NOW, NATE!

HEY! NO FAIR! THE ZOMBIES ARE ATTACKING DINO-PIG! WE HAVE TO HELP!

GIMME A SECOND. THERE'S ONE LAST SLICE...

BANCITY-BANG!

KRANCITTY-KRANNG!

KRANNG!

KA-KOOM!

KOOM! BANG!

BOOM

BANG!

BOOM

BANG!

KRANNG!

NO! MY BEAUTIFUL, MASSIVE, MUNCH MACHINE! THIS ISN'T THE END OF THIS!

SQUICK!

EH?

PLOP

BLOOP

PLANTS vs. ZOMBIES™

THE LADY IN RED

Written by **PAUL TOBIN**
Art by **BRIAN CHURILLA**
Letters by **STEVE DUTRO**

Celebrating 15 Years
FREE COMIC BOOK DAY™

The Free Comic Book Day story that
introduced Nate's Shroompoo Shampoo!

It was a cruel and vicious case, the kind that can ruin a man.

The kind of story that makes you stare deep into your soul and wonder where everything's gone wrong.

SHROOMPOO...
FOR THAT CLEAN-SMELLING MUSHROOM SCENT!

It was the kind of case where you always keep your squirt gun close.

The kind of case that always seems to start with a lady in red knocking on my office door.

KNOCK KNOCK

NATE! YOU *IN* THERE?

Yeah. I was in there. I was also in trouble, and I knew it. The girl's name was Patrice, and everything about her was trouble. She looked like trouble. Smelled like trouble.

KNOCK KNOCK KNOCK

Meanwhile, I looked like I would need a shave in five or six years, and I smelled like mushrooms because of my favorite shampoo.

Ten minutes later, we were on the streets. There was no time for small talk, or sweet talk, or for any talk at all except making a call to the boys.

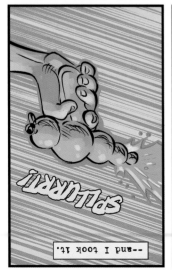

CREATOR BIOS

Paul Tobin Ron Chan Matt J. Rainwater Steve Dutro

PAUL TOBIN is a critically acclaimed freckled person who has a detailed plan for any actual zombie invasion, based on creating a vast perfume and cologne empire—both of which would be vitally important in a zombie-infested world. Paul was once informed he "walks funny, like, seriously," but has recovered from this childhood trauma to write hundreds of comics for Marvel, DC, Dark Horse, and many others, including such creator-owned titles as *Colder* and *Bandette*, as well as *Prepare to Die!*—his debut novel. His *Genius Factor* series of novels about a fifth-grade genius and his war against the Red Death Tea Society began in March 2016 from Bloomsbury Publishing. Despite his many writing accomplishments, Paul's greatest claim to fame is his ability to win water levels in *Plants vs. Zombies* without using any water plants.

RON CHAN is a comic book and storyboard artist, video game fan, and occasional jujitsu practitioner. He was born and raised in Portland, Oregon, where he still lives and works as a member of the local artist collective Periscope Studio. His comics work has been published by Dark Horse, Marvel, and Image Comics, and his storyboarding work includes boards for 3D animation, gaming, user-experience design, and advertising for clients such as Microsoft, Amazon Kindle, Nike, and Sega. He really likes drawing Bonk Choys. (He also enjoys eating actual bok choy in real life.)

Residing in the cool, damp forests of Portland, Oregon, **MATT J. RAINWATER** is a freelance illustrator whose work has been featured in advertising, web design, and independent video games. On top of this, he also self-publishes several comic books, including *Trailer Park Warlock*, *Garage Raja*, and *The Feeling is Multiplied*—all of which can be found at MattJRainwater.com. His favorite zombie-bashing strategy utilizes a line of Bonk Choys with a Wall-nut front guard and Threepeater covering fire.

STEVE DUTRO is a comic book letterer from northern California who can also drive a tractor. He graduated from the Kubert School and has been in the comics industry for decades, working for Dark Horse (*The Fifth Beatle*, *I Am a Hero*, *The Evil Dead*, *Eden*), Viz, Marvel, and DC. Steve's last encounter with zombies was playing zombie paintball in a walnut orchard on Halloween. He tried to play the *Plants vs. Zombies* video game once but experienced a full-on panic attack and resolved to stick with calmer games . . . like *Gears of War*.